The ups & downs of being a PET OWNER

The ups & downs of being a PET OWNER

Tony Husband

ARCTURUS

The cover image and cartoons on pages 7, 8, 11, 15, 14, 17, 19, 26, 32, 34, 35, 36, 48, 58, 66, 71, 77, 87, 94, 95, 97, 107, 124, 124, 125, 127 are reproduced by kind permission of **PRIVATE EYE** magazine – www.private-eye.co.uk/Tony Husband

ARCTURUS

This edition published in 2016 by Arcturus Publishing Limited
26/27 Bickels Yard, 151–153 Bermondsey Street,
London SE1 3HA

ISBN: 978-1-78599-704-4
AD005258UK

Printed in China

INTRODUCTION

I've had pets all my life from a child growing up on a smallholding with lovely friendly pigs, comical hens, goats, geese and ducks, as well as a collection of mice, rats, cats and dogs. The cats and dogs were ours; the mice and rats were not. I've never had a time of more than a month or so when I didn't have a dog.

My first real animal mate was Rebel, a little terrier who worshipped me and I him. We roamed the hills and woods together. He slept on the end of my bed, and waited for me as I walked up the country lane from school. Strangely, I don't remember his demise. Perhaps the mind of a small boy couldn't absorb such sadness, but I do remember his life.

Others followed. Sally, Kim, Mouse, Sooty, Gollum, Bowser, Kelly, Sheena, and now Seve – a lorryload of dogs, all characters, all devoted friends. The most recent, Seve, is a rescue dog named after my golfing hero Seve Ballesteros. We got Seve the week Seve the golfer passed away. I took Seve on my local golf course a couple of weeks later. I let the dog off his lead and he immediately vanished. So here's me on a golf course a couple of weeks after the golfer had died shouting, 'Seve, come back… Seve, get here now.' Strange looks from all corners!

Seve is wonderful with our grandchildren Pheobe and Daisy; they love him to bits and he loves all the attention they give him.

Pets have given me lots of lovely memories and some sad ones of course. We all know that final trip to the vet's and the tearful goodbye. So this book contains lots of animal jokes. Some you may recognize; others you will find just plain silly. And I've stuck in a few wild animals too because this is a small world and nothing wild (or what is left of so many amazing creatures) is really wild anymore.

Tony Husband

'Your cat keeps doing its business in my garden.'

'He loves retrieving the frisbee... It just takes so long.'

8

'I hate the way the cat plays with
every mouse he catches.'

'Well, I think someone should tell the poor old chap
his dog died two weeks ago.'

'He's having trouble with his motions.'

'Yes, thank you, Duxbury, he's fine,
but I've not called you in here to talk about my goldfish.'

'Looks like the mouse poison worked.'

'Dear Mum, I've got a friend...'

'Yes, he's very good, but we don't get much call for stunt penguins.'

'My earrings!!? My husband won them at a fair.'

'I told you the DVD machine was faulty.'

'God, it does my head in...
Why do they stare at us all the time?'

'Cash?... Ta, mate, that'll do nicely.'

'Ignore him. He's always on the cadge.'

'Stop that hamster!!!'

'You spoil that cat.'

'You'll have to excuse my husband,
he was brought up by wolves.'

'I can't stop swearing, Father.'

'You can't fool me, Harry. The bird's dead, isn't he?'

'Don't worry. It's an old sign.'

'The new MD's ruthless I've heard...'

'Colin's trying to create a no-fly zone.'

'I'm being neutered. Apparently, it means having my nails clipped.'

'Well, I don't call it heaven when we're not allowed
to sniff each other's bottoms.'

'We're on the lookout for sheep rustlers.
Have you three lads seen anything suspicious?'

33

'I thought you gave them an injection.'

'Fraud squad.'

'Yes?'

'This is quite amazing.
It seems the female gorilla is knitting me a cardigan.'

'No... it's Charlie that got an eagle,
not an eagle that got Charlie.'

'Have you fed the birds today?'

'He's a miner bird.'

'The catflap? Yes, George is a big fan of Westerns.'

'Waiter!'

A pigeon fancier

'We think he's swallowed the cat.'

'I wouldn't normally come out on a Christmas Eve...'

'I could watch the fish for hours.' 'You do!'

'Sorry. It's just I don't trust anybody in a shell suit.'

'It's for you.'

'It's the best I could do for him. I suddenly hit bedrock.'

'Let me through. It's an emergency.'

'Yes!'

'Don't panic. He's showing affection.'

'Not the most adventurous of hunters, is he?'

'It's a text from the babysitter:
"Really sorry, the gerbil's had an accident."'

'Hey, what's all the hullabaloo?'

'Hi, missus. Got any ants need eating?'

'The hamster loves driving around in my remote control car, Dad.'

'I don't think stamping on it will do much good, dear.'

'I was advised to get an animal I could bond with.'

3
THE FOUR
WISE MEN

'What?'

DOGS THAT LOOK LIKE
THEIR OWNERS COMPETITION

'I see a fish coming towards you... Oh, sorry, wrong globe.'

'Could I have my dog back please?'

'Retreat... they have the advantage of height.'

'Mum, Dad... what do you mean I'm adopted?'

'That *was* hilarious when he said he'd get his big brother.'

'Groan! We drank too much last night.'

'Can't say the linesman is filling me with confidence.'

'It doesn't look like the mole traps worked.'

'I'm thinking of joining a gym.'

'Well, it looks like a molehill.'

'Can you tell next door his python's escaped again?'

'Ow... I put a foreign coin in and it bit me.'

'You say your cat does tricks... Just how big is this cat?'

'Can you come home right away?
The tortoise is in one of his moods.'

'We have to eat Billy.'

'That's me before my plastic surgery.'

'It's Cheetah, Jane. He's in trouble.'

'Watching the development of tadpoles into frogs might be an
interesting project, but not in my bath it's not.'

'Love the concept, hate the dog.'

'Best all-round sheepdog I ever had.'

'Wow, it's my wife... Great news: the guinea pig's had six babies!'

'What's got into the sheep?'

'Mummy, I think Grandad might have fallen in the tank
with the piranhas.'

'Oi, get lost.'

'I always have fish on Friday.'

'I need a second opinion. He's delusional. He's been imagining he's a hippo ever since he found he was covered in tick birds.'

'I have a flea circus... Yes, I scratch a living.'

'All patrols, keep a lookout for an elephant that's escaped
from the circus.'

'Stop following me.'

'I was sat watching my flock last night all seated on the ground.
The glory of the Lord came down and scared me half to death...'

'He got it on eBay.'

'I think you're overfeeding this fish.'

'Rescued at last, but I'm not leaving without the wife and kids.'

'Aagh!! There's a spider in the bath.'

'Run, they lost again.'

'Good boy... where have you buried Mummy?'

'Auntie Betty sat on Morris, my pet mouse!!'

'Here we go... Just be careful where you sit.
Our pet scorpion's escaped.'

'You hid your Viagra in the hamster cage?!!'

'I wonder what they did wrong.'

'Harvey, have you electrified the birdbath again?'

'Does he talk?'

'That dog's got fleas.'

'I went further south this time.'

'Shiver me timbers, Polly, that was close!'

'Oh, for God's sake,
stay still.'

'For goodness sake, Martin, it's only a couple of snails.'

'You spoil that goldfish.'

'Just exactly what kind of food are you putting out for the birds?'

'Can you call back? He's having a catnap.'